This journal belongs to:

My zodiac stone is:

Published in the UK by Scholastic, 2023
1 London Bridge, London, SE1 9BG
Scholastic Ireland, 89E Lagan Road, Dublin Industrial Estate,
Glasnevin, Dublin, D11 HP5F

SCHOLASTIC and associated logos are trademarks
and/or registered trademarks of Scholastic Inc.

Text by Laura Baker & Emily Stead © Scholastic, 2020, 2023
Designed by Cloud King Creative
Images used under license from Shutterstock.com

ISBN 978 07023 2985 2

A CIP catalogue record for this book is available from the British Library.

Printed and bound in Italy by L.E.G.O S.p.A
Paper made from wood grown in sustainable forests and other controlled sources.

2 4 6 8 10 9 7 5 3 1

www.scholastic.co.uk

My Crystal Zodiac Journal

This Crystal Zodiac Journal takes you through the year with the stars by your side. Discover your zodiac sign, your special stone, your lucky day and more. There are crafts, activities and a magical recipe to try, too. Learn about each zodiac sign, then record your year, filling in your special memories under each sign.

It's time to sparkle!

Welcome to the cosmos!

Astrology is the interpretation of stars, planets and other celestial bodies: in particular, their movements in the sky and how these affect the universe – including you!

People all around the world have been studying different types of astrology for thousands of years. They find stories in the stars and pass them down through the generations. These stories are often about gods and goddesses, who rule different parts of the sky. Today, we call these stories 'mythology', and many of the planets are named after ancient gods and goddesses.

Astrologers believe that the movements of the stars, planets and Moon in the sky shapes our personalities. How we get on with others is said to be written in the stars, while our personal challenges are affected by these celestial bodies too.

Knowing your sun sign, or zodiac sign, will help you discover more about your cosmic portrait. Your sun sign depends on the position of the Sun in the sky when you were born. Each sign has also been linked to special gemstones since ancient times. These stones are believed to have protecting and healing properties, to benefit both mind and body.

Turn the page to begin your cosmic journey!

You star!

What is your zodiac sign? And what does it say about you? Read the pages that follow to help you fill in this cosmic profile **STARRING** you.

My name: --

My birthday: ------------------------------------

My zodiac sign: ---------------------------------

My zodiac stone: --------------------------------

My lucky day: -----------------------------------

My element:
   earth   air   water   fire

Three personality traits of my zodiac sign
that sound just like me:

1. -

- -

2. -

- -

3. -

- -

Two challenges of my zodiac sign that sound just like me:

1. -

- -

2. -

- -

The zodiac

The zodiac is a flat map of the sky, often laid out in a circle as if it were wrapped around the Earth. It is divided into 12 sections. Each section was defined by a constellation found in that part of the sky, thousands of years ago. The 12 signs of the zodiac are: Aries, Taurus, Gemini, Cancer, Leo, Virgo, Libra, Scorpio, Sagittarius, Capricorn, Aquarius and Pisces.

Each sign has one or more special zodiac stones, natural treasures from the earth. Wearing or keeping your zodiac crystal close to your body is said to help boost your energy. So which stone is special to your zodiac sign?

Aries (bloodstone)   Taurus (sapphire)

Gemini (agate)   Cancer (emerald)

Leo (onyx)   Virgo (carnelian)

Libra (opal)   Scorpio (aquamarine)

Sagittarius (citrine)   Capricorn (ruby)

Aquarius (garnet)   Pisces (amethyst)

The zodiac is an astrologer's lens for viewing and reading the universe. Just how do you fit in?

Read on!

Aries

Birthday: 21st March–19th April

Zodiac stone: bloodstone

Alternatives: diamond, aquamarine, tiger's eye

Element: fire

Lucky day: Tuesday

If your birthday falls from 21st March to 19th April, Aries is your zodiac sign. Being the first sign of the zodiac, **Ariens** know how to get things started. They jump straight in, thrilled by a new challenge. The red-flecked gem bloodstone helps those born under **Aries** move forwards on their journey with certainty, offering the wearer protection.

Personality traits:

assertive, independent, competitive, courageous, energetic,

spontaneous, passionate, honest, generous

Challenges for Ariens:

★ **Ariens** move so fast that they can get bored easily!

★ **Ariens** are very straightforward, and may sometimes have trouble connecting with people who are less upfront.

★ **Ariens** are miles ahead of everyone else, so may need to wait for others to catch up.

★ Don't let them slow you down, **Aries** – hold on to your sense of self!

Celestial symbols

Every zodiac sign
has its own symbol.
Did you spot yours?

Most signs are animals, mythical creatures
or people. The symbol for **Aries** is
a ram with large, curved horns.

Every symbol has a meaning. For example,
the **Pisces** symbol is two fish swimming
in different directions. This shows that
Pisceans are open to change and always moving.

Libra is the only zodiac sign that is not
represented by an animal or a person.
The scales show **Libra's** need for balance.

If you could create a new sign to suit you perfectly,
what would it be? Sketch your own celestial symbol below –
you could choose a mythical creature, an animal or something
that represents your best traits.

My Aries diary

21st March–19th April

How did you challenge yourself under the *Aries* sun this year? Write your weekly highlights here.

21st–27th March

28th March–3rd April

4th–10th April

_____

_____

_____

_____

_____

11th–19th April

_____

_____

_____

_____

_____

Taurus

Birthday: 20th April–20th May

Zodiac stone: sapphire

Alternatives: aventurine, clear quartz, topaz

Element: earth

Lucky day: Friday

If your birthday falls from 20th April to 20th May, Taurus is your zodiac sign. Taureans are grounded, practical and ruled by their senses. The sign's main stone, sapphire, commonly sparkling blue, makes a great match for Taureans, aiding self-expression and honesty. This stone has a deep connection with the planet, a trait shared by those born under earth sign Taurus.

Personality traits:

loyal, stubborn, determined, practical, resourceful,

cautious, methodical, sensible

Challenges for Taureans:

★ **Taureans** think practically. If they give advice to someone who doesn't take practical steps to get out of a muddle, **Taureans** can quickly become impatient!

★ **Taureans** don't like change and can be hesitant to leave their comfort zone. They can sometimes think material things are the most important thing in life.

★ Remember, **Taureans**, let your inner sparkle shine out loud!

Grow a garden!

Love the earth like a Taurus!

You don't need loads of outdoor space to go green.
Try growing a garden on your window sill!

You will need:

★ tin cans (carefully rinsed and dried)

★ herb seeds (from your local garden centre or DIY shop)

★ felt-tip pens

★ thin card

★ PVA glue

★ potting soil

1. Collect your cans. You'll need one for each different type of herb you'd like to plant. You could start with three and build up to as many as will fit on your window sill!

Star tip:

Ask an adult to help you in case of sharp edges, then remove the labels and carefully rinse out the cans.

coriander

2. Cut out a card label for each of your cans. Write the name of the herb you will be planting on each one. Use strong PVA glue to stick a label on to each can. Leave to dry.

3. Place potting soil in each can, filling to about one centimetre below the rim.

4. Add several herb seeds to each can. Push the seeds down into the soil with your finger. Follow the instructions on the different herb packets for the best results.

5. Pour a little water into each can, allowing it to soak into the soil. Stop watering when water sits on top of the soil.

6. Place your herb cans on a sunny window sill. Remember to keep watering them regularly.

Star tip:
Crystals don't just heal humans – amethyst, rose quartz and tourmaline may energize poorly plants, while jasper can encourage new growth.

My Taurus diary

20th April–20th May

What trials did you tackle under the
Taurus sun this year? Write your tests
and triumphs here.

20th–26th April _____

27th April–3rd May _____

4th May-10th May ---------------------------------------

11th May-20th May ---------------------------------------

Gemini

Birthday: 21st May–20th June

Zodiac stone: agate

Alternatives: pearl, tourmaline, citrine

Element: air

Lucky day: Wednesday

If your birthday falls from 21st May
to 20th June, Gemini is your zodiac sign.
Busy, busy, busy – Geminis are always on the go!
They are the life and soul of the party, charming and
playful. Amazing agate, the main gem of Geminis,
can balance the twin personalities of this sign, and
help with communication and confidence.

Personality traits:

curious, clever, restless, changeable, chatty, playful, silly, adaptable, unpredictable, adventurous

Challenges for Geminis:

★ **Geminis** are so sociable and chatty that they might not click with quieter signs. They need to find friends who can keep up!

★ Being interested in so many things, **Geminis** can often appear unpredictable or uncommitted as they move to the next exciting thing.

★ **Geminis** sometimes rush around so much that they can become frazzled and forgetful. Remember to slow down and find time for your sparkly self, **Gemini**!

Party planning

Channel social-butterfly *Gemini* and plan a party — for a birthday, a special occasion or just because! Choose a theme and then make everything else match.

- ☐ Crystal celebration
- ☐ Afternoon tea time
- ☐ Movie mania
- ☐ Trinket treasure hunt
- ☐ Other: _____

- ☐ Adventure in nature
- ☐ Karaoke sing-along
- ☐ Craft and create
- ☐ Sporting challenge

Plan your menu. What will you serve? Think about drinks and food that match your theme.

_____
_____
_____

Star tip:
Get creative with your food design. For example, if you're having an crystal-themed party, you could cut each sandwich into a cute crystal shape!

Deck the halls. Which decorations will you choose for your party? Jot down some ideas here. _ _ _ _ _ _ _ _ _ _ _ _ _ _ _ _ _ _ _

_ _

_ _

Design your own invitation or make copies of the invite on this page. Fill in the details and share with all your friends. ↘

You are invited to my party!

Date: _

Time: _

Place: _

RSVP to: _ _ _ _ _ _ _ _ _ _ _ _ _ _ _ _ _ _

My Gemini diary

21st May–20th June

How did you sparkle under the *Gemini* sun?
Did you try anything new? Keep a record
of activities and events here.

21st–27th May _____

_____

_____

_____

28th May–3rd June _____

_____

_____

_____

_____

4th-10th June _____

_____

_____

_____

_____

11th-20th June _____

_____

_____

_____

Cancer

Birthday: 21st June–22nd July

Zodiac crystal: emerald

Alternatives: ruby, moonstone, carnelian

Element: water

Lucky day: Monday

If your birthday falls from 21st June to 22nd July, Cancer is your zodiac sign. Those born under **Cancer** float along on feelings, picking up on the emotions of anyone around them. Emerald, the stone of eternal love, helps **Cancerians** forge happy friendships and strong bonds with family. The stone can balance emotions for this super cautious water sign, too.

sensitive, family-oriented, caring, protective, thoughtful, nurturing, loyal, suspicious, worrisome

Challenge for Cancerians:

★ **Cancerians** can sometimes be a bit crabby – they are the crab, after all – but they are also very loving.

★ They can get cosy in their comfort zones and often retreat into their shells when they feel threatened. Once they feel safe, though, they'll be right there for you.

★ **Cancerians** can, at times, become possessive of their close family and friends. Remember: sharing is caring!

My family tree

Explore your family history like a caring Cancerian.

Grandparents

Name: _____
Zodiac sign: _____
Zodiac crystal: _____

Name: _____
Zodiac sign: _____
Zodiac crystal: _____

Name: _____
Zodiac sign: _____
Zodiac crystal: _____

Name: _____
Zodiac sign: _____
Zodiac crystal: _____

Parents

Name: _____
Zodiac sign: _____
Zodiac crystal: _____

Name: _____
Zodiac sign: _____
Zodiac crystal: _____

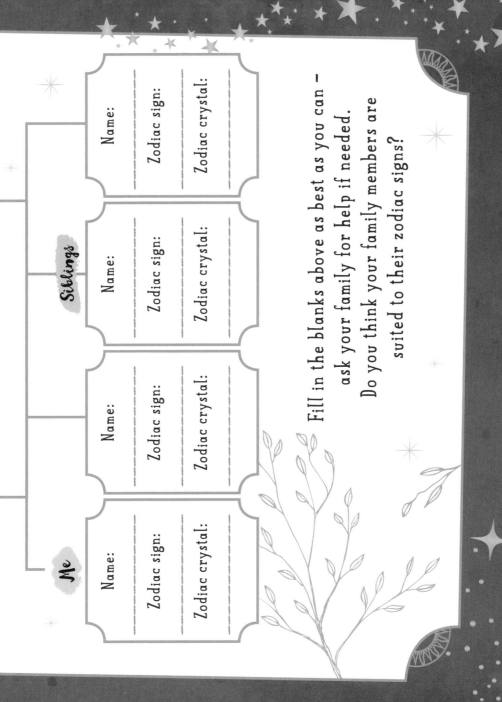

Siblings

Name:

Zodiac sign:

Zodiac crystal:

Name:

Zodiac sign:

Zodiac crystal:

Name:

Zodiac sign:

Zodiac crystal:

Me

Name:

Zodiac sign:

Zodiac crystal:

Fill in the blanks above as best as you can – ask your family for help if needed. Do you think your family members are suited to their zodiac signs?

My Cancer diary

21st June–22nd July

Who did you connect with under the *Cancer* sun?
Record memorable meetings with family
and friends here.

21st June–27th June _____

_____

_____

_____

28th June–4th July _____

_____

_____

_____

_____

5th July—11th July _

_ _

_ _

_ _

_ _

12th July—22nd July _

_ _

_ _

_ _

_ _

35

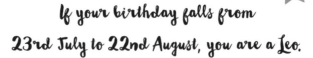

Leo

Birthday: 23rd July–22nd August

Zodiac crystal: peridot

Alternatives: sunstone, carnelian, ruby

Element: fire

Lucky day: Sunday

If your birthday falls from
23rd July to 22nd August, you are a Leo.
Ruled by the sun and fire, it's no surprise that Leos
are shining stars! Glimmering green peridot encourages
Leos to share the limelight, and not just lap up all the praise
for themselves. Such natural performers, there's simply
no need for these wildcats to envy others!

Personality traits:

optimistic, outgoing, passionate, showy, ambitious, friendly, warm, brave, fierce, strong, proud, dramatic

Challenges for Leos:

★ With their love of the spotlight, Leos can sometimes make it all about themselves.

★ Leos know their worth, so they need to find friends who value them.

★ Leos don't always like to share the stage. Keep your jealousy at bay and you'll shine even brighter, Leo!

Hidden gems

Look around you and you'll discover you're in sparkling company! Stick in pics or doodle your shimmering cast of friends and family below.

Most loyal
friend ever

Funniest
person
I know

Most likely to discover
a new planet

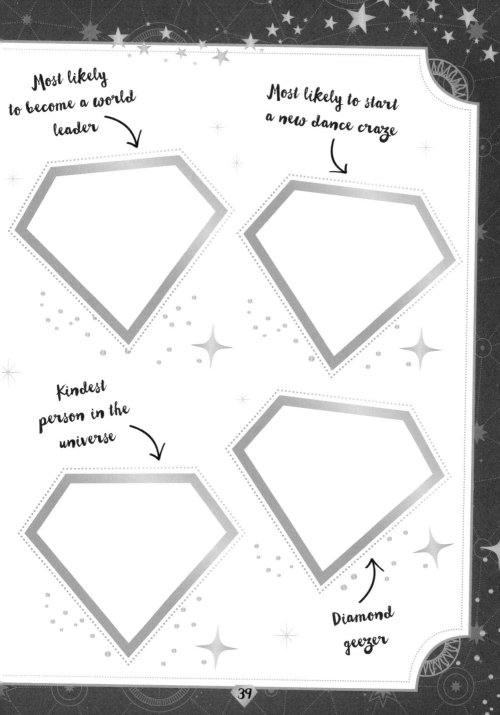

Most likely to become a world leader

Most likely to start a new dance craze

Kindest person in the universe

Diamond geezer

My Leo diary

23rd July–22nd August

Did the sunny stone for **Leo** help you shine this
month? Write down some warming moments.

23rd July–29th July _____
_____
_____
_____
_____

30th July–5th August _____
_____
_____
_____
_____

6th August–12th August _
_ _
_ _
_ _
_ _

13th August–22nd August _
_ _
_ _
_ _
_ _

Virgo

Birthday: 23rd August–22nd September

Zodiac crystal: carnelian

Alternatives: sapphire, garnet, peridot

Element: earth

Lucky day: Wednesday

If your birthday falls from 23rd August to 22nd September, Virgo is your zodiac sign..

Virgos just love to analyse and organize, studying every detail to untangle a problem that the cosmos may throw their way. Carnelian, which inspires creativity, is perfect for these clever problem-solvers. This reddish stone can fire up Virgos if their self-belief begins to drop too.

Personality traits:

perfectionist, smart, clever, practical, organized,
logical, helpful, thoughtful, quiet

Challenges for Virgos:

★ **Virgos'** love of detail can sometimes lead them to
overthink things, which can cause worries.

★ **Virgos** can feel shaken if their routine is disrupted.
They need to remember to breathe and give themselves
a break.

★ **Virgos** sometimes expect life to live up to the perfect
image they have in their head, while the reality doesn't
always match. Try to go with the flow, **Virgo!**

My top fives

Super-organized *Virgo* loves a list! Fill in your top fives to keep track of your picks of the moment.

My top five favourite zodiac crystals:

1. _____
2. _____
3. _____
4. _____
5. _____

My top five favourite people:

1. _____
2. _____
3. _____
4. _____
5. _____

Five things I want to do before the end of the year:

1. _____
2. _____
3. _____
4. _____
5. _____

Now think of a category of your own.

My top five _____ :

1. _____
2. _____
3. _____
4. _____
5. _____

My Virgo diary

23rd August–22nd September

What were your biggest accomplishments under the Virgo sun? What were you most proud of, at school or at home? Record your highs here.

23rd August–29th August _____

_____

_____

_____

30th August–5th September _____

_____

_____

_____

_____

6th September–12th September _

_ _

_ _

_ _

_ _

13th September–22nd September _

_ _

_ _

_ _

_ _

Libra

Birthday: 23rd September–22nd October

Zodiac crystal: opal

Alternatives: topaz, peridot, jade

Element: air

Lucky day: Friday

If your birthday falls from 23rd September to 22nd October, Libra is your zodiac sign.. Their shimmering zodiac stone of opal helps to bring balance and harmony – just what a *Libran* craves! This lucky crystal can support *Librans* to make good decisions, earning the love and respect of family, friends and teammates. Let your light shine, *Libra!*

Personality traits:

balanced, fair, diplomatic, impartial, mediating, charming, peaceful, agreeable, indecisive

Challenges for Librans:

★ If a situation can't balance perfectly, Librans might find it hard to choose one side over another.

★ Librans can sometimes appear to be avoiding deeper issues, as they focus on creating lovely balance on the surface.

★ With their natural need to find peace, Librans can get drawn into other people's problems. Choose the causes that are important to you, Libra, to keep your own scales balanced!

Perfect poetry

Librans' love of balance often leads them to the arts, where harmony can create beautiful things. Write a beautifully balanced acrostic poem, describing yourself using the letters of your zodiac sign.

What is an acrostic poem? An acrostic poem starts with a vertical word, then uses each letter of that word to begin a line of the poem. For example:

L oves opal

I ndecisive

B alanced

R esourceful

A ll they want is peace!

Star tip:
Each line can be a phrase or simply a word. It's up to you! You can even use a letter from the main word in the middle of a line if you get stuck.

It's your turn! Craft your own cosmic acrostic.

Write the letters of your zodiac sign, with each letter starting a new line. Then complete the lines with poetry all about **you!**

My Libra diary

23rd September–22nd October

How did you achieve harmony under the Libra sun this year? Write the challenges you encountered and your personal breakthroughs here.

23rd September–29th September _____

_____

_____

_____

30th September–5th October _____

_____

_____

_____

6th October–12th October _____

_____

_____

_____

_____

13th October–22nd October _____

_____

_____

_____

_____

Scorpio

Birthday: 23rd October–21st November

Zodiac stone: aquamarine

Alternatives: topaz, citrine, agate

Element: water

Lucky day: Tuesday

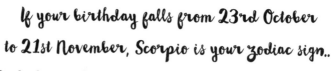

If your birthday falls from 23rd October to 21st November, Scorpio is your zodiac sign.. Dark, deep and secretive, a sensitive nature lies beneath a **Scorpio's** hard exterior. Aquamarine makes a perfect zodiac stone for this water sign, helping to soften the sign's fiery sting. Known as the 'Stone of Courage', this crystal offers **Scorpios** the confidence to try new things.

Personality traits:

mysterious, deep, intense, secretive, powerful, ambitious, hardworking, dedicated, stubborn

Challenges for Scorpios:

★ Though they appear tough, deep down **Scorpios** are not invincible. They sometimes let their emotions get the better of them.

★ **Scorpios** can have trouble letting go, and will hold a grudge to the end of the cosmos.

★ **Scorpios** can be wary of anyone they meet. Open yourself up to new friends, **Scorpio**, and you never know what adventures will come your way!

Crystal cookies

Make these gorgeous, glittering crystal cookies to share with your friends and family. Don't share the recipe, though – keep it your little secret, like a *Scorpio* would!

You will need:

★ non-stick baking paper

★ 150 g butter

★ 75 g golden caster sugar

★ 2 tsp vanilla extract

★ 1 egg

★ 300 g flour

★ crystal-shaped cutter

★ 150 g white chocolate

★ gold and silver sprinkles

1. Ask an adult to pre-heat the oven to 180°C (160°C fan). Line two baking trays with non-stick baking paper.

Star tip: Ask an adult to supervise when using the oven and microwave.

2. Cream the butter, sugar and vanilla extract together in a mixing bowl until smooth. Add the egg and continue to mix, gradually adding the flour until you form a soft dough. Wrap in cling film and chill for 30 minutes.

3. Roll out the dough until it is ½ cm thick on a board dusted with a little flour. Cut out crystal shapes using a cutter or freehand. Place on the baking trays and bake for about 15 minutes until golden brown. Remove from the oven and cool on a wire rack.

4. Break up the chocolate and place in a heatproof bowl. Microwave on medium for one minute at a time, stirring the chocolate after each minute until it has melted.

5. To decorate, drizzle the chocolate over the top of the biscuits. Add the sprinkles, then leave to set.

6. Share your snacks for a truly

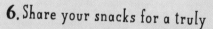

magical treat!

My Scorpio diary

23rd October–21st November

What secrets did you discover about yourself
under the Scorpio sun? Write your revelations here.

23rd October–29th October _ _ _ _ _ _ _ _ _ _ _ _ _ _ _ _ _ _ _

_ _

_ _

_ _

_ _

30th October–5th November _ _ _ _ _ _ _ _ _ _ _ _ _ _ _ _ _ _ _

_ _

_ _

_ _

_ _

6th November–12th November _

_ _

_ _

_ _

_ _

13th November–21st November _

_ _

_ _

_ _

_ _

Sagittarius

Birthday: 22nd November–21st December

Zodiac stone: turquoise

Alternatives: citrine, blue topaz

Element: fire

Lucky day: Thursday

If your birthday falls from 22nd November to 21st December, Sagittarius is your zodiac sign. Sagittarians are always looking for their next adventure. Give them room to roam, and they'll go far — exploring places as well as ideas. On the flip side, Sagittarians could try to be more considerate. Their zodiac stone, turquoise, has a purifying effect and is useful for encouraging empathy.

adventurous, energetic, enthusiastic, independent, positive, honest, clever, funny, impatient

Challenges for Sagittarians:

★ With a **Sagittarius**, everything becomes bigger than when it started, which sometimes leads them to exaggerate.

★ Super-honest **Sagittarians** need to be careful not to offend their friends with their words.

★ **Sagittarians'** adventures can lead them in many directions. Follow your passion, **Sagittarius**, and you'll blaze a trail behind you!

Secret stone

Which zodiac stone could help to heal you?
Take this quiz to discover your secret stone. It may
be different from your actual zodiac stone!

	hopeful	I am happiest when...
How are you feeling today?	annoyed	What do you sometimes struggle with?
	worried	Which emotion would you like to feel more often?
	relaxed	Which activity appeals to you?

I spend time in nature.	agate
I'm doing something creative.	citrine
I'm helping others.	opal
I give up too easily.	bloodstone
Keeping my energy levels up.	ruby
Speaking up in class or groups.	emerald
A little more confidence.	carnelian
Calmness would be nice.	turquoise
Who couldn't use more love?	garnet
Splashing about in water.	aquamarine
Puzzles and brain games.	sapphire
Yoga and meditation.	onyx

My Sagittarius diary

22nd November–21st December

What adventures did you have under the
Sagittarius sun? Write down your memorable
moments – big or small – below.

22nd November–28th November _ _ _ _ _ _ _ _ _ _ _ _ _ _ _ _

_ _

_ _

_ _

29th November–6th December _ _ _ _ _ _ _ _ _ _ _ _ _ _ _ _ _

_ _

_ _

_ _

7th December–13th December _____

_____

_____

_____

_____

14th December–21st December _____

_____

_____

_____

_____

Capricorn

Birthday: 22nd December–19th January

Zodiac stone: ruby

Alternatives: rose quartz, garnet, emerald

Element: earth

Lucky day: Saturday

If your birthday falls between **22nd December**
and **19th January**, **Capricorn** is your zodiac sign.
When a **Capricorn** is feeling negative or down, ruby's rich
red colour brings confidence, courage and joy. As **Capricorns**
are the hardest-working sign of the zodiac, rubies are said
to help increase stamina and restore energy levels. Rubies
will have you raring to go, **Capricorn!**

ambitious, driven, responsible, realistic, precise,
determined, mature, strong leader

Challenges for Capricorns:

★ **Capricorns** like to focus on the future, which means they can sometimes forget to consider others in the present.

★ **Capricorns** often work so hard that they forget to have fun. Try to find the right balance between work and play.

★ **Capricorns** tend to dwell on the negatives. Remember to look for the positives too, **Capricorn**, and the world is yours! Go shine!

Putting plans in place

Capricorns are super driven and like to see real results. Take a leaf from their book and set some goals for the year ahead to reach your own superstar status.

Goal 1:

At school, I want to _____

by _____ (date).

I know I'll have reached my goal when I can _____

_____

Things I can do to help me reach my goal:

_____

_____

_____

_____

Star tip:

Set goals that you can realistically achieve by a certain date – it will feel amazing when you reach them! Have your zodiac stone close by to keep up your energy levels.

Goal 2:

At home, I want to _____

by _____ (date).

I know I'll have reached my goal when I can _____

_____

Things I can do to help me reach my goal: _____

_____

_____

_____

Goal 3:

As a person, I want to _____

by _____ (date).

I know I'll have reached my goal when I can _____

_____

Things I can do to help me reach my goal: _____

_____

_____

My Capricorn diary

22nd December–19th January

Did your charming crystals give you
a boost of energy this month? Write
about your little wins here.

22nd December–28th December _ _ _ _ _ _ _ _ _ _ _ _ _ _

_ _

_ _

_ _

29th December–4th January _ _ _ _ _ _ _ _ _ _ _ _ _ _

_ _

_ _

_ _

_ _

5th January–11th January

12th January–19th January

Aquarius

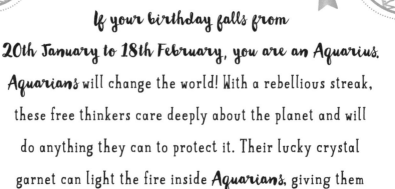

Birthday: 20th January–18th February

Zodiac stone: garnet

Alternatives: amethyst, bloodstone, onyx

Element: air

Lucky day: Saturday

If your birthday falls from 20th January to 18th February, you are an Aquarius. Aquarians will change the world! With a rebellious streak, these free thinkers care deeply about the planet and will do anything they can to protect it. Their lucky crystal garnet can light the fire inside **Aquarians**, giving them the courage they need to make a difference.

friendly, kind, original, honest, loyal, stubborn,

changeable, independent, aloof

Challenges for Aquarians:

★ While **Aquarians** are so focused on their cause,
they can appear unfriendly to friends and family.

★ **Aquarians** need a positive place to focus their
rebellious ideas.

★ They move to their own beat. Others may not understand,
but you know you're going places, **Aquarius!**

Be the change

Aquarians love to protect the world around them. What can you do to help your planet? Tick the suggestions you will try below. Then write your own planetary pledge.

This year I will:

- [ ] try to walk, bike or scoot instead of making car journeys
- [ ] use reusable bags instead of plastic ones when shopping
- [ ] swap to bars of soap and shampoo, along with bamboo toothbrushes to reduce throwaway plastic
- [ ] mend clothes instead of throwing them away
- [ ] have a clothes swap with friends to get a new look without buying new clothes
- [ ] turn off lights, devices and taps when not in use
- [ ] recycle and compost as much as possible

Star tip: Get your family involved in trying these ideas, too!

My planetary pledge

This year I promise to help my planet by:

1. _____

_____

2. _____

_____

3. _____

_____

4. _____

_____

5. _____

_____

Signed: _____

Date: _____

My Aquarius diary

20th January–18th February

Gleaming garnet, the stone of Aquarius, inspires passion. Show how you put your passion for the planet into practice this month.

20th January–26th January _ _ _ _ _ _ _ _ _ _ _ _ _ _ _ _ _
_ _
_ _
_ _

27th January–2nd February _ _ _ _ _ _ _ _ _ _ _ _ _ _ _
_ _
_ _
_ _
_ _

3rd February–9th February _

_ _

_ _

_ _

_ _

10th February–18th February _

_ _

_ _

_ _

_ _

Pisces

Birthday: 19th February–20th March

Zodiac Stone: amethyst

Alternatives: aquamarine, jasper

Element: water

Lucky day: Thursday

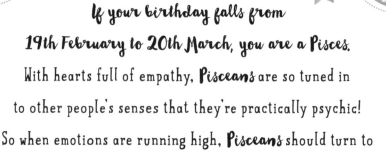

If your birthday falls from 19th February to 20th March, you are a Pisces. With hearts full of empathy, **Pisceans** are so tuned in to other people's senses that they're practically psychic! So when emotions are running high, **Pisceans** should turn to the soothing crystal amethyst. Trust in the power of purple to help spark creativity, too!

Personality traits:

sensitive, creative, artistic, dreamy, empathetic, spiritual, intuitive, detail-focused, impulsive

Challenges for Pisceans:

★ **Pisceans** would rather live in the clouds than in reality!

★ **Pisceans** are highly sensitive and can get attached very easily. They need to find friends who will be there for them.

★ **Pisceans** may go along with others to avoid getting hurt. Believe in your superstar self, **Pisces!**

Sparkle jar

Dream like a Pisces!

Make a jar to hold all your hopes, dreams and inspirations. Then take them out each time you need a reminder of your cosmic potential.

You will need:

★ a large jar, with lid

★ coloured paper

★ scissors

★ glue

1. Choose a jar that's large enough to hold your notes, then carefully clean and dry your jar.

2. Ask an adult to help you cut out crystal shapes from your coloured paper. Glue these around the outside of your jar.

3. Cut out the notes on the opposite page. Fold them, then pop them in your jar.

4. Over time, add more notes with your own words of wisdom, and your hopes and dreams.

Take out a note to read whenever you need to add a little sparkle to your day!

Shoot for the stars.

Something special is about to happen.

For others to believe in you,
first believe in yourself. .

Never stop smiling.

Kindness is a superpower.

You are out-of-this-world wonderful.

Be brave. Be different. Be you.

Spread a little sparkle wherever you go.

Every challenge helps you to grow.

Every mistake helps you to learn.

Hope never goes out of style.

Dream big, sparkle more, shine brightly.

Mystical mindfulness

Take time to slow down and focus. Colour these
cool crystals. Doodle more stars, too.
Colour... and breathe.

My Pisces diary

19th February–20th March

What did you dream about under the Pisces sun?
Were your dreams crystal clear? Write about the
ones you can remember below.

19th February–25th February _ _ _ _ _ _ _ _ _ _ _ _ _ _ _ _ _ _

_ _

_ _

_ _

26th February–3rd March _

_ _

_ _

_ _

4th March–10th March

_____

_____

_____

_____

_____

11th March–20th March

_____

_____

_____

_____

_____

Caring for your crystals

An important part of keeping your crystals in tip-top condition is remembering to cleanse them, to remove any negative energy stored within the stones.

You can cleanse many hard stones (amethyst, agate, citrine, carnelian, quartz and ruby) by running them under water for a minute or two. Water that flows naturally, such as a stream, is an ideal place, but you can cleanse these stones under a running tap too.

Avoid cleansing delicate gems such as turquoise or opal using hot or salty water, though, as they may start to dissolve. Instead, leave these stones in the glowing moonlight to help them charge up again.

Star tip:
A full moon can work wonders in restoring crystals, as the lunar energy is at its most powerful.

Storing your crystals

Keep your crystals in a safe place, wrapped in a soft
cloth or pouch to avoid dust, scratches or damage.
Your stones will be ready the next time you need them!

Stone: _____   Date cleansed: _____

Stone: _____   Date cleansed: _____

Stone: _____   Date cleansed: _____

Stone: _____   Date cleansed: _____

Star tip:
Try to cleanse and charge
your crystals about once
a month. Keep a record
of this ritual for
each stone.

Mystical matches

The personality traits of certain zodiac signs complement each other well. These zodiac signs are likely to be fast friends – a match made in the cosmos!

Your zodiac sign:	Your best friends:				
	Aries	Taurus	Gemini	Cancer	Leo
Aries			◆		◆
Taurus				◆	
Gemini	◆				◆
Cancer		◆			
Leo	◆		◆		
Virgo		◆		◆	
Libra	◆		◆		◆
Scorpio		◆		◆	
Sagittarius	◆		◆		◆
Capricorn		◆		◆	
Aquarius	◆		◆		◆
Pisces		◆		◆	

See who you click with using this chart. Find your own zodiac sign down the left side of the grid, then read across to discover your zodiac compatibilities. For example, **Aries** is most compatible with **Gemini, Leo, Libra, Sagittarius** and **Aquarius.**

Your best friends:						
Virgo	Libra	Scorpio	Sagittarius	Capricorn	Aquarius	Pisces
	◇		◇		◇	
◇		◇		◇		◇
	◇		◇		◇	
◇		◇		◇		◇
	◇		◇		◇	
		◇		◇		◇
			◇		◇	
◇				◇		◇
	◇				◇	
◇		◇				◇
	◇		◇			
◇		◇		◇		

Phases of the moon

The moon goes through different phases as it travels around our planet. In astrology, each phase has its own energy. Note when you spot these phases in the sky.

New Moon: reflection, setting intentions
Crystals to keep close: quartz, citrine, moonstone
Date phase spotted: _ _ _ _ _ _ _ _ _ _ _ _ _ _ _ _

Waxing crescent: breakthrough, taking action
Crystals to keep close: rose quartz, aventurine
Date phase spotted: _ _ _ _ _ _ _ _ _ _ _ _ _ _ _ _

First quarter:
planning, organizing
Crystals to keep close:
tiger's eye, carnelian
Date phase spotted:

_ _ _ _ _ _ _ _ _ _ _ _ _ _ _

Star tip:
Set your goals and intentions on the New Moon. Then see them develop through the moon's phases, over about 28 days.

Waxing gibbous: questioning, perfecting
Crystals to keep close: citrine, pyrite
Date phase spotted: _ _ _ _ _ _ _ _ _ _ _ _ _ _ _ _ _ _

Full Moon: clarity, discovery
Crystals to keep close: moonstone, onyx
Date phase spotted: _ _ _ _ _ _ _ _ _ _ _ _ _ _ _ _ _

Waning gibbous: communicating, accomplishing
Crystals to keep close: clear quartz, amethyst
Date phase spotted: _ _ _ _ _ _ _ _ _ _ _ _ _ _ _ _ _ _

Third quarter: seeing results
Crystals to keep close: black tourmaline
Date phase spotted: _ _ _ _ _ _ _ _ _ _ _ _ _ _ _ _ _

Waning crescent: closure, reflection
Crystals to keep close: bloodstone, aquamarine
Date phase spotted: _ _ _ _ _ _ _ _ _ _ _ _ _ _ _ _ _ _

Looking back

That's a whole zodiac year over! What did you learn about yourself as you journeyed through the stars? Write your memories and ambitions here.

The top three things I achieved this year:

1. ------------------------------------

2. ------------------------------------

3. ------------------------------------

Three things I would like to achieve next year:

1. ------------------------------------

2. ------------------------------------

3. ------------------------------------

A new crystal I got: ------------------------------

A new crystal I hope to get next year: ------------------

Stick mementos on to this page:
ticket stubs, secret notes or even superstar selfies!